"Don't go pet a porcupine"

Poems About Animals

Chosen by Gervase Phinn

W

FRANKLIN WATTS
LONDON•SYDNEY

This edition 2003

First published in 2001 by
Franklin Watts
96 Leonard Street
London EC2A 4XD

Franklin Watts Australia
45–51 Huntley Street
Alexandria NSW 2015

© In this anthology Gervase Phinn 2001

A CIP catalogue record for this book is
available from the British Library.

ISBN 0 7496 4950 X

Series Editor: Louise John
Designer: Robert Walster

Dewey Classification 821.008

Printed in Hong Kong/China

Picture Credits

Niall Benvie/OSF: 26-27
Mary Cantrille/RSPCA: 23
Martyn Colbeck/OSF: 5
Bruce Coleman Inc/Bruce Coleman Collection: 12, 28
Stephen Dalton/NHPA: 11
E A James/RSPCA: 29
Johnny Johnson/Bruce Coleman Collection: 6-7
Gerard Lacz/Frank Lane Photo Agency: 14-15
Manfred Pfefferle/OSF: 30
Andy Rouse/NHPA: 24
Jany Sauvanet/NHPA: cover, 1, 2, 25
Kim Taylor/Bruce Coleman Collection: 18, 22, 31
Jim Watt/Bruce Coleman Collection: 19
Gunter Ziesler/Bruce Coleman Collection: 9
Daniel Zupanc/NHPA: 20
Robert Walster: 17

Acknowledgments

The editor and publishers gratefully acknowledge permission to reproduce the following copyright material. Every effort has been made to trace copyright, but if any omissions have been made, please let us know in order that this may be corrected in the next edition.

'Elephants Dreaming' by John Agard, from 'We Animals Would Like A Word With You' published by Bodley Head in 1990. © John Agard. Reprinted by permission of John Agard, c/o C. Sheldon Literary Agency.
'A Big Bare Bear' by Robert Heidbreder, from 'Don't Eat Spiders'. © 1999 by Robert Heidbreder. Reprinted by permission of Stoddart Publishing Co. Limited.
'Fancy Me' by Janet Paisley, from 'Twinkle, Twinkle Chocolate Bar' published by Oxford University Press. © Janet Paisley. Reprinted by permission of the author.
'If I Were a Frog' by Trevor Millum, from 'Warning – Too Much Schooling Can Damage Your Health'
published by Nelson. © Trevor Millum. Reprinted by permission of the author.
'Black Dot' by Libby Houston, from 'All Change!' by Libby Houston, published by Oxford University Press in 1993. © Libby Houston, 1993. Reprinted by permission of the author.
'Charlotte's Dog' by Kit Wright, from 'Cat Among the Pigeons' by Kit Wright (Viking Kestrel 1987.) Copyright © Kit Wright 1984, 1987. Reprinted by permission of Penguin Books Limited.
'To My Dog' by Adrian Mitchell, from 'Balloon Lagoon and the Magic Islands of Poetry' published by Orchard Books. © Adrian Mitchell. Reprinted by permission of Peters Fraser & Dunlop on behalf of Adrian Mitchell. **Educational Health Warning! Adrian Mitchell asks that none of his poems are used in connections to any examination whatsoever.**
'Cat Began' by Andrew Matthews, from 'Paws and Claws' published by Hutchinson. © Andrew Matthews. Reprinted by permission of Peters Fraser and Dunlop on behalf of Andrew Matthews.
'My Uncle Paul of Pimlico' by Mervyn Peake. Reprinted by permission of David Higham Associates Ltd.
'Stickleback' by Ted Hughes, from 'The Cat and the Cuckoo' by Ted Hughes, published by Faber and Faber. Reprinted by permission of Faber and Faber Ltd.
'The Shark' by Lord Alfred Douglas (cut by one stanza). Reprinted by permission of Sheila Colman, The Lord Alfred Douglas Literary Estate.
'Question Time' by Michaela Morgan. © Michaela Morgan. Reprinted by permission of the author.
'In the Stable: Christmas Haiku' by Michael Harrison, from 'Junk Mail' by Michael Harrison published by Oxford University Press in 1993. © Michael Harrison 1993. Reprinted by permission of the author.
'The Donkey' by G K Chesterton. Reprinted by permission of A P Watt Limited on behalf of The Royal Literary Fund.
'If Pigs Could Fly' by James Reeves, from 'Complete Poems for Children' published by Heinemann.
© James Reeves. Reprinted by permission of the James Reeves Estate, c/o Laura Cecil Literary Agency.
'Who to Pet and Who Not to' by X J Kennedy. © 1975 by X J Kennedy
'Otter' by Brian Carter, from 'Carnival of Animals' edited by Sybil Marshall and published by Cambridge University Press. © Brian Carter. Reprinted by permission of the author.
'Rhinoceros' by Matt Simpson, from 'Sandwich Poets – Matt, Wes and Pete, published by Macmillan.
© Matt Simpson. Reprinted by permission of the author.
'A Yak From The Hills of Iraq' by Willard R Espy, in 'The Best of an Almanac of Words at Play' by Willard R Espy, published by Merriam-Webster Inc.
© Willard R Espy 1999. Reprinted by permission of Merriam-Webster Inc.
'The Praying Mantis' by Dick King-Smith, from 'Alphabeasts' published by Cassell. Reprinted by permission of A P Watt Limited on behalf of Fox Busters Limited.
'Spider' by Barbara Juster Esbensen, from 'Words With Wrinkle Knees' published by Oxford University Press in 1990. © Barbara Juster Esbensen. Reprinted by permission of Mr T Esbensen.

Contents

Elephant

Elephant, death-bringer!
Elephant, spirit of the bush!
      With his one hand he brings two trees to the ground.
If he had two hands, he would tear the sky like an old rag.
Spirit who eats dog!
Spirit who eats ram!
Spirit who eats palm-fruit, thorns and all!
With four pestle-legs he flattens the grass,
Where he walks, the grass cannot stand again.
An elephant is no load for an old man –
Not even for a young man!

Yoruba, Nigera

Elephants Dreaming

On a marvellous grey morning
A mountain is beginning to breathe.
Each rock shudders with long memories.
The sun blows her yellow trumpet
Over a hunter asleep with his gun.
O what a beautiful day for a stampede.

John Agard

My Monstrous Bear

When I was small,
My father would pretend to be a monstrous bear.
He'd crawl about the floor on all fours
And his great ferocious eyes
Would stare and glare, searching for me.
He'd roar and roar
And growl and grunt,
And I would hide behind the chair,
And squeal and squirm
And feel the hair on my head stand up,
Excited in my fear.
He'd pretend not to see me
And lumber off and curl up on the rug
And snore and snore.
I would creep so quietly
And snuggle up, deep between his great warm paws.
My monstrous bear would hold me tightly
Keeping me from harm.

Gervase Phinn

A Big Bare Bear

A big bare bear
    bought a bear balloon,
For a big bear trip
    to the bare, bare moon.
A hairy bear
    saw the bare bear fly
On the big bear trip
    in the bare, bare sky.
The hairy bear
    took a jet up high
To catch the bear
    in the big bare sky.
The hairy bear
    flew his jet right by
The bear balloon
    in the big bare sky.
He popped the balloon
    with his hairy thumb,
And the bare bear fell
    on his big bum bum.

Robert Heidbreder

Fancy Me

A wee creepy crawly
crawled and creeped
along the leafie through.
He splished and splashed
past dibbly drops
of wishy washy dew.
And down the bendy bough
he chomped,
champing willy-nilly.
Until he felt
his tummyfull
was gurgling giggly-silly.

Worry me, he cried
and curled
into a safely spot.
And snoozing soft,
he slept and slept
snizzling quite a lot.

The winkly sun
tickled his tum
and woke him up to see
wings and things
and traily bits
bobbling round him free.

He stretched and fell
into the sky,
a flittering, floating
butterfly
who didn't think
of quizzling why
but just said,
Fancy me.

Janet Paisley

8

If I Was a Frog...

If I was a frog, I'd hop
Out of my chair and some people would scream.
If I was a jelly-fish, I'd flop
On the floor and when someone trod on me
They'd slide across the room
And land with a clump on their backside.
If I was an albatross I'd flap
My wings and look knowingly
As people fled outside.
If I was a seal, I'd clap
My flippers and look shiny and cute
As people smiled and wished
They could have a miniature one of me
In their fish pond or padding pool.
And if I was a –
        but as I'm human,
The most advanced species
Ever to walk, hop or flop, flap or slip
Across the face of the earth
I'll just sit here waiting for the bell to ring.

Trevor Millum

Black Dot

a black dot
a jelly tot

a scum-nail
a jiggle-tail

a cool kicker
a sitting slicker

a panting puffer
a fly-snuffer

a high hopper
a belly-flopper

a catalogue
            to make me
                        frog

Libby Houston

The Tyger

Tyger! Tyger! burning bright
In the forests of the night,
What immortal hand or eye
Could frame thy fearful symmetry?

In what distant deeps or skies
Burnt the fire of thine eyes?
On what wings dare he aspire?
What the hand dare seize the fire?

And what shoulder, and what art,
Could twist the sinews of thy heart?
And, when thy heart began to beat,
What dread hand? and what dread feet?

What the hammer? what the chain?
In what furnace was thy brain?
What the anvil? what dread grasp
Dare its deadly terrors clasp?

When the stars threw down their spears,
And water'd heaven with their tears,
Did he smile his work to see?
Did he who made the Lamb make thee?

Tyger! Tyger! burning bright
In the forests of the night,
What immortal hand or eye,
Dare frame thy fearful symmetry?

William Blake

Charlotte's Dog

Daniel the spaniel has ears like rugs,
Teeth like prongs of electric plugs.

His back's a thundery winter sky,
Black clouds, white clouds rumbling by.

His nose is the rubber of an old squash ball
Bounced in the rain. His tail you'd call

A chopped-off rope with a motor inside
That keeps it walloping. Red-rimmed-eyed,

He whimpers like plimsolls on a wooden floor.
When he yawns he closes a crimson door.

When he barks it's a shark of a sound that bites
Through frosty mornings and icy nights.

When he sleeps he wheezes on a dozing lung:
Then he wakes you too with a wash of his tongue!

Kit Wright

To My Dog

This gentle beast
this golden beast
laid her long chin
along my wrist

and my wrist
is branded
with her love
and trust

and the salt of my cheek
is hers to lick
so long as I
or she shall last

BY
~~Adrian Mitchell~~
Josh WILSON

Cat Began

Cat began.
She took the howling of the wind,
She took the screeching of the owl
And made her voice.

For her coat
She took the softness of the snow,
She took the yellow of the sand,
She took the shadows of the branches of the trees.

From deep wells
She took the silences of stones,
She took the moving of the water
For her walk.

Then at night
Cat took the glittering of stars,
She took the blackness of the sky
To make her eyes.

Fire and ice
Went in the sharpness of her claws
And for their shape
She took the new moon's slender curve –

And Cat was made.

Andrew Matthews

16

My Uncle Paul of Pimlico

My Uncle Paul of Pimlico
Has seven cats as white as snow,
Who sit at his enormous feet
And watch him, as a special treat,
Play the piano upside-down,
In his delightful dressing-gown;
The firelight leaps, the parlour glows,
And, while the music ebbs and flows,
They smile (while purring the refrains),
At little thoughts that cross their brains.

Mervyn Peake

Stickleback

The Stickleback's a spiky chap,
    Worse than a bit of briar.
Hungry Pike would sooner swallow
    Embers from a fire.

The Stickleback is fearless in
    The way he loves his wife.
Every minute of the day
    He guards her with his life.

She, like him, is dressed to kill
    In stiff and steely prickles,
And when they kiss, there bubbles up
    The laughter of the tickles.

Ted Hughes

The Shark

A treacherous monster is the Shark,
He never makes the least remark.

And when he sees you on the sand,
He doesn't seem to want to land.

He watches you take off your clothes,
And not the least excitement shows.

His eyes do not grow bright or roll,
He has astounding self-control.

And when towards the sea you leap,
He looks as if he were asleep.

But when you once get in his range,
His whole demeanour seems to change.

He throws his body right about,
And his true character comes out.

It's no use crying or appealing,
He seems to lose all decent feeling.

After this warning you will wish
To keep clear of this treacherous fish.

His back is black, his stomach white,
He has a very dangerous bite.

Lord Alfred Douglas

Question Time

What does a monster look like?
     Well . . .hairy
and scary,
and furry,
and burly and pimply and dimply and warty and naughty
and wrinkled and crinkled ...
That's what a monster looks like.

How does a monster move?
It oozes,
it shambles,
it crawls and it ambles, it slouches and shuffles and trudges, it lumbers
and toddles, it creeps and it waddles ...
That's how a monster moves.

Where does a monster live?
In garden sheds,
under beds,
in wardrobes, in plug holes and ditches,
beneath city streets, just under your feet ...
That's where a monster lives.

How does a monster eat?
It slurps and it burps and gobbles and gulps and sips and swallows and
scoffs, it nibbles and munches, it chews and it crunches ...
That's how a monster eats.

What does a monster eat?
Slugs and bats and bugs and rats and stones and mud and bones and blood
and squelchy squids ... and nosy kids.
YUM!
That's what a monster eats!

Michaela Morgan

In the Stable: Christmas Haiku

Donkey
My long ears can hear
Angels singing, but my song
Would wake the baby.

Dog
I will not bark but
Lie, head on paws, eyes watching
All these visitors.

Cat
I wash my feet. For
This baby all should be clean.
My purr will soothe him.

Owl
My round eyes look down.
No starlit hunting this night:
Peace to little ones!

Spider
My fine web sparkles:
Indoor star in the roof's night
Over the baby.

Michael Harrison

The Donkey

When fishes flew and forests walked,
And figs grew upon thorn,
Some moment when the moon was blood
Then surely I was born;
With monstrous head and
      sickening cry
And ears like errant wings,
The devil's walking parody
On all four-footed things.

The tattered outlaw of the earth,
Of ancient crooked will;
Starve, scourge, deride me: I am dumb,
I keep my secret still.

Fools! For I also had my hour;
One far fierce hour and sweet:
There was a shout about my ears,
And palms before my feet.

G K Chesterton

If Pigs Could Fly

If pigs could fly, I'd fly a pig
To foreign countries small and big –
To Italy and Spain,
To Austria, where cowbells ring,
To Germany, where people sing –
And then come home again.

I'd see the Ganges and the Nile;
I'd visit Madagascar's isle,
And Persia and Peru.
People would say they'd never seen
So odd, so strange an air-machine
As that on which I flew.

Why, everyone would raise a shout
To see his trotters and his snout
Come floating from the sky;
And I would be a famous star
Well known in countries near and far –
If only pigs could fly!

James Reeves

Who to Pet and Who not to

Go pet a kitten, pet a dog,
Go pet a worm for practice,
But don't go pet a porcupine –
You want to be a cactus?

X J Kennedy

Otter

Sun-flickery
in his coat of many bubbles
he melts into water,
seldom troubles to rise for air,
an oil-slickery streak
of brilliantine, there
below the surface:
a shimmer below the glimmer
and spangle of summer,
a swirl with a tail,
a stain, a shadow
oil-slickery in his trickery
of dodges and feints
and dives and bubbly delvings.

Yet in the field all yickery
he lolloped, less than a dog,
lay like a rough old log
in the sun, dry as a stick;
and I ached to toss him in the pool,
to see him wed to water,
doing his sleekings, slick,
to his own satisfaction
in dark liquefication.

Brian Carter

Rhinoceros

God simply got bored and started doodling
with ideas he'd given up on, scooping off the floor
bits and bobs and sticking them together:
the tail of a ten-ton pig he'd meant for Norway
the long skull of a too-heavy dinosaur,
the armour plating of his first version of
the hippo, an unpainted beak of a toucan
stuck on back to front, a dash of tantrums
he intended for the Abyssinian owl, the same
awful grey colour he'd used for landscaping the moon.

And tempted to try it with the batteries,
he set it down on the wild plains of Africa,
grinned at what he saw and let it run.

Matt Simpson

A Yak from the Hills of Iraq

A yak from the hills of Iraq
Met a yak he had known awhile back.
    They went out to dine,
    And talked of lang syne –
Yak-ety, yak-ety, yak.

Willard R Espy

The Praying Mantis

The praying mantis seems to be
Intent on its devotions,
And yet its intellect is free
Of all religious notions.

The mantis male thinks, in a daze
Of love, 'I'll court and win her!'
But when he has, the female preys.
She snaps him up for dinner.

Dick King-Smith

Spider

Her silken name
woven   fine as light
is fastened to the edges
of the page

Where she spins
the word hangs   a letter
at a time   S P I D E R
sticky   anchored against
the wind's breath   waiting

Eight legged spinner word
swift-running   weaver word
fast biting   tight-wrapping
get-the-broom-quick   word
S P I D E R!

Barbara Juster Esbensen

Index of First Lines